CW00394028

Marc

Sigmund
Freud

Pisolo
Books

A SHORT INTRODUCTION OF PSYCHOANALYSIS WRITTEN & ILLUSTRATED BY A PSYCHIATRIST

www.marcobonafede.com

Copyright: Marco Bonafede
Translated by Leo Ortolano
ISBN: 978-88-907438-3-2

Special thanks to Christopher Schembri

THE PERSON YOU SEE SITTING HERE IS
SIGMUND FREUD, A DOCTOR BORN AT THE
BEGINNING OF THE CENTURY IN VIENNA.
HIS NAME IS PRONOUNCED "FROYD"

ALL OF YOU SHOULD KNOW BY NOW
UNLESS YOU HAVE BEEN HIDING UNDER A
ROCK SOMEWHERE.

THIS IS A SOFA, THERE FREUD USED
TO LAY HIS PATIENTS DOWN WHILE
LISTENING TO THEIR PROBLEMS.
IS THE SOFA INDISPENSABLE?

CERTAINLY NOT, BUT FREUD DID NOT LIKE
TO BE OBSERVED WHILE HIS PATIENTS
WERE IN SESSION.

FINALLY
I CAN PICK
MY NOSE!

BLA BLA
BLA BLA
BLA BLA
BLA BLA

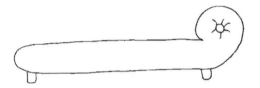

FREUD WAS TIRED OF PSYCHOLOGY'S POOR DESCRIPTIONS. HE WANTED TO UNDERSTAND "WHY" A PERSON'S PSYCHIC EQUILIBRIUM WAS DAMAGED.

TO ACCOMPLISH THIS FREUD DECIDES TO
GO DEEP INTO THE DARK SIDE OF THE
HUMAN BEING.

NOT COUNTING MORALISM, IT WAS
NECESSARY TO UNDERSTAND WHAT WAS
HIDING DEEP IN THE PATIENTS' MINDS.

THEN HE FOUND OUT:

HE FOLLOWS THE PLEASURE'S PRINCIPLE

BUT QUICKLY CHANGES HIS MIND.

IN PRACTICE HE IS THE MOST SYMPATHETIC COMPONENT OF THE PSYCHE.

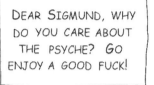

ALL THE RESTRICTIONS A PERSON HAS RECEIVED FROM THE SURROUNDING ENVIRONMENT ARE INTERNALIZED IN THE SUPER-EGO.

AND WHAT IS THE SUPER-EGO?

WHAT DO YOU MEAN DOC FREUD, YOU SURPRISE ME! CAN YOU IMAGINE WHAT SOCIETY WOULD BE WITHOUT ME? WHAT IF I WAS NOT AROUND TO KEEP THAT SCOUNDREL OF AN ID IN LINE?

IT IS THIS FEELING OF PLEASURE THAT MAKES HIM EXPLORE THE WORLD!

AND STICK EVERYTHING IN HIS MOUTH.

THE CHILD FEELS PLEASURE BY STIMULATION OF THE ANAL MUCOSA ALSO...

DISGUSTING!

ONLY LATER THE ATTENTION GOES TO HIS
GENITALS.

AND WHO MIGHT YOU BE?

WOW! YOU GIVE ME SENSATIONAL FEELINGS!

I HAVE SHOWN YOU THE DEVELOPING OF LIBIDO'S
THREE STAGES: **ORAL STAGE**, **ANAL STAGE** AND
GENITAL STAGE.

WHAT'S **LIBIDO**?

COME, I WILL INTRODUCE YOU TO HER!

OF COURSE! I'M THE FORCE THAT MEN USE TO FIND PLEASURE, THE ENERGY USED TO SATISFY THEIR **DRIVES** IN OTHER WORDS THEIR INSTINCTS.

THROUGH SOME STAGES THEY LEARN HOW TO GET PLEASURE FROM THEIR BODY AND REACH THE GENITAL STAGE.

HE IS A TYPICAL EXAMPLE OF THE ORAL TYPE!
IN THE EARLY CHILDHOOD, HE FELT
VERY INTENSE SATISFACTION IN SUCKING
AND IS STILL LINKED TO ORAL PLEASURES!

THIS INDIVIDUAL IS DEPENDENT, A PESSIMIST AND ALWAYS LOOKING FOR SUPPORT. IN CONTRAST TO THE OTHER ONE HE NEVER FULFILLED HIS NEEDS WHILE HE WAS BREAST FEEDING.
HE IS ALWAYS AFRAID HE WILL BE LEFT STARVING!

INSTEAD WHEN AN INDIVIDUAL IS TOO TIDY, CONSCIENTIOUS, THRIFTY THEN HE IS AN **ANAL CHARACTER**.

MY MOMMY ALWAYS TOLD ME: HOW CLEAN AND NEAT MY CHILD IS! NOBODY DOES LITTLE TURDS IN THE POTTY LIKE HIM !

WHEN I WAS LITTLE, MAMA AND PAPA DID NOT ALLOW ME TO DO ANYTHING.
NOW IT IS ME WHO ORDERS OTHERS AROUND! YOU SHOULD KNOW HOW TO CONTROL YOUR INSTINCTS AS I HOLD IN MY OWN SHIT!

THERE IS NOTHING MORE BEAUTIFUL THAN A WELL-MAINTAINED MILITARY BASE AND A BATTLE FIELD FULL OF GLORIOUS FALLEN SOLDIERS WITH THEIR GUTS HANGING OUT. IT IS WONDERFUL TO DIE FOR YOUR COUNTRY!

WHAT A PIECE OF WORK!

EIN, ZWEIN !

EIN, ZWEIN !

EIN, ZWEIN !

YES, HE IS VERY FRUSTRATED!

...AND THE **GENITAL CHARACTER?**

THEORETICALLY IT SHOULD BE THAT OF A HEALTHY PERSON, BALANCED AND THAT HAD REACHED EMOTIONAL MATURITY. IN REALITY EVERY PERSON HAS SOME ORAL AND SOME ANAL CHARACTERISTICS. GOT IT?

THINK ABOUT THIS! WHAT IS MORE IMPORTANT FOR A HUMAN BEING THAN EATING AND PROCREATING? NOTHING! THEY ARE ESSENTIAL FUNCTIONS!

SURE...

THEN WHY ARE YOU WONDERING ABOUT THE FACT THAT THE MOST IMPORTANT AREAS FROM THE PLEASURE POINT OF VIEW ARE THOSE ORALS, ANALS AND GENITALS?

...BUT THIS CAN'T BE DEFINED AS SEXUAL PLEASURE! YOU HAVE SEX WITH ANOTHER PERSON AND NOT ALONE WITH YOURSELF!

BRILLIANT OBSERVATION, DOC. FREUD, YOU'RE RIGHT! IN FACT THE INFANTILE SEXUAL PLEASURE IS **NARCISSISTIC** IN OTHER WORDS ORIENTED TOWARDS THEMSELVES.

INSTEAD ADULT'S SEXUALITY IS ORIENTED TOWARD THE PARTNER!

BUT TO REACH THIS POINT THERE IS A NECESSARY PREPARATORY PHASE, AN APPRENTICESHIP: THE INFANTILE SEXUALITY! GOT IT?

YES, BUT WHEN DO YOU START THINKING ABOUT THE PARTNER?

EVERY CHILD GOES THROUGH THIS PHASE WHERE THE
SEXUAL DESIRE MOVES FROM THEMSELVES TO THE PARENT'S
BODY OF THE OPPOSITE SEX.
THE CHILD FALLS IN LOVE WITH
THE MOTHER AND FEELS
JEALOUSY TOWARDS
THE FATHER!

THE CHILD FEELS PLEASURE FROM
TOUCHING HIS MOTHER'S BODY...

BUT HE FINDS OUT HE CAN'T DO IT WHILE HIS
FATHER IS GETTING ATTENTION FROM THE MOTHER.
THEN HE WISHES HIS FATHER AWAY, DEAD,
TO HAVE HIS MOTHER ALL FOR HIMSELF.

NO, IT IS ONLY NATURAL! INSIDE THE FAMILY NUCLEUS THE CHILD LEARNS THE WORLD AND ITS DIFFICULTIES.

HE LEARNS "I WANT" THAT HE WILL NEVER GET...

HE LEARNS THAT HIS MOTHER ISN'T ONLY FOR HIM, BUT HE HAS TO SHARE HER WITH HIS FATHER AND HIS SIBLINGS.

HE LEARNS TO
KNOW AUTHORITY...

AND HE WILL
LEARN TO REVOLT!

PRRR!

HE WILL LEARN THAT TO REVOLT ALSO HAS A PRICE!

IN PRACTICE THE CHILD TRAINS HIMSELF TO GET ALONG WITH OTHER HUMAN BEINGS!

THEN IS THE OEDIPUS COMPLEX SYMBOLIC?

YES...

...LUCKILY! I WOULDN'T THINK SO!

IT IS SYMBOLIC, BIOLOGICAL AND SEXUAL. DON'T YOU FORGET IT!

...UHM, EXCUSE ME MR. UNCONSCIOUS: THIS NAME, OEDIPUS, IS NOT NEW TO ME...

YOU DID CLASSICAL STUDIES, DIDN'T YOU?

YES.

OEDIPUS IS THE MAIN CHARACTER OF A GREEK'S FAMILY TRAGEDY.
OEDIPUS KILLS HIS FATHER, NOT KNOWING HE WAS HIS FATHER, AND MARRIED HIS MOTHER, NOT KNOWING SHE WAS HIS MOTHER. HIS DRAMA REPRESENTS THAT OF ALL CHILDREN!

EXCUSE ME MR. UNCONSCIOUS BUT WHAT YOU ARE SAYING IS ONLY ABOUT BOYS! WHAT ABOUT GIRLS?

THE GIRLS HAVE THE ELECTRA COMPLEX, SIMILAR TO OEDIPUS: THEY FALL IN LOVE WITH THEIR FATHER AND WISH THE MOTHER'S DEAD.

THE GIRLS ALSO HAVE
OTHER PROBLEMS:
FOR EXAMPLE,

PENIS ENVY

> I CAN PEE AGAINST THE
> WALLS AND YOU CAN'T!

BUT IT IS BETTER NOT TO TALK ABOUT THIS.
THESE THEORETICAL EXAMPLES WILL GIVE YOU
PROBLEMS WITH FEMINISTS ...

> WHAT ARE
> FEMINISTS ?

> IT IS COMPLICATED TO EXPLAIN,
> IT IS A THING FROM THE FUTURE.

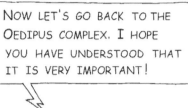

NOW LET'S GO BACK TO THE OEDIPUS COMPLEX. I HOPE YOU HAVE UNDERSTOOD THAT IT IS VERY IMPORTANT!

WELL...

DOCTOR FREUD, WAKE UP!

THE OEDIPUS COMPLEX REPRESENTS THE BATTLE BETWEEN THE PLEASURE PRINCIPLE, THAT COVERS THE CHILDREN'S WORLD, AND THE REALITY PRINCIPLE, THAT COVERS THE ADULTS'S WORLD!

THIS CONFLICT HAS TO BE RESOLVED
FROM THE CHILD TRANSFORMING
HIMSELF IN OEDIPUS,
"KILLING THE FATHER"...

...OR BEING CRUSHED BY PATERNAL AUTHORITY

...THEN IT
WILL BE SNIPPED!

MR. UNCONSCIOUS YOU SCARE ME...

AS I SCARE MANY PEOPLE THAT CARRY INTERNAL CONFLICTS INSIDE OF THEM...

...THAT ALWAYS RESURFACE PROMPTING THE PSYCHIC'S DISTRESS, UNHAPPINESS AND...

...NEUROSIS!

OH MY GOD! WHERE THE HELL AM I?

THE ID CONTINUOUSLY PROVIDES DESIRES AND THE SUPER-EGO CENSORS THEM.

IF THE ID INSISTS, BEATING WILL INCREASE. **ANXIETY** IS THE RESULT, A VERY UNPLEASANT FEELING THAT WARNS THE EGO ABOUT THE ONGOING CONFLICT.

THE EGO RUSHES IN TO STOP THE BRAWLING WITH MEDIATION!

BUT, IF THE MEDIATION FAILS, WHAT IS LEFT IS TO CONTROL THE ID!

AND WILL IT SUCCEED?

VERY OFTEN. THE EGO HAS DIFFERENT METHODS TO HELP CURB THE ID. ONE OF THESE IS **DISPLACEMENT.**

...THAT IS TO TURN THE SEXUAL DESIRE TOWARD ANOTHER GOAL. FOR EXAMPLE: TO DEDICATE THE LIBIDINAL ENERGY TOWARD A HOBBY SUCH AS STAMP COLLECTING!

YES DOCTOR! THE EGO HAS CHANNELED THE SEXUAL DESIRE INTO ARTISTIC CREATION!

ALTRUISTIC ACTIVITIES AND SOCIAL
USEFULNESS SUCH AS TAKING CARE OF
SICK PEOPLE AND MISSIONARY WORK
ARE RESULT FROM SUBLIMATION!

REPRESSION IS CARRIED OUT BY SOME SORT OF COPS USED BY THE SUPER-EGO, THAT INTERVENES IN REPRESSING VERY STRONG DESIRES.

THEIR DUTY IS TO STOP INTENSE SEXUAL DESIRES FROM REACHING THE CONSCIOUSNESS.

REPRESSION IS A VERY IMPORTANT
DEFENSE MECHANISM.
ALWAYS ON DUTY, ALSO UNPLEASANT
THOUGHTS AND MEMORIES
ARE IMPRISONED BY ITS COPS.

IT IS A MECHANISM THAT DOESN'T
WASTE TIME IN KEEPING THE PSYCHIC
BALANCE BUT IT IS ALSO DANGEROUS...

IN FACT THE SEXUAL DESIRE CAN EVEN
MAKE ITS VOICE HEARD FROM PRISON

AND IS VERY SKILLFUL IN ESCAPING!

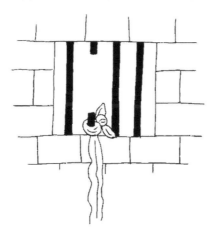

THE ESCAPED EGO IS NOW VERY FURIOUS
AND IS READY TO FACE THE SUPER-EGO,
FIGHTING AGAINST HIM EVERY INCH
OF THE WAY...

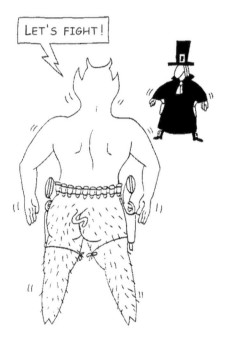

NOW THERE IS NO POSSIBLE MEDIATION!

IT DEPENDS ON THE REASON FOR FIGHTING BUT ALSO ON ANOTHER FACTOR: HAVE YOU SEEN A FIGHT BETWEEN TWO PEOPLE WHO HAVE KNOWN EACH OTHER A LONG TIME? WELL, THE FIGHTING IS STRONGER IF THESE TWO HAVE SOMETHING TO THROW AT EACH OTHER, FOR EXAMPLE BRINGING UP WRONG DOINGS BETWEEN EACH OTHER FROM THE PAST.

IN OTHER WORDS, IN THE CONFLICT BETWEEN THE EGO AND SUPER-EGO THE INFANTILE PSYCHIC LIFE COMES OUT!

THEN CAN'T THE CONFLICT BE RESOLVED?

YES! IT IS RESOLVED: EGO AND SUPEREGO COME TO AN AGREEMENT BETWEEN THEMSELVES WITH COMPROMISE...

DEAR DOCTOR, I WILL SHOW YOU THE FAMOUS
MOTHER-IN-LAW CASE. A YOUNG MAN INTRODUCED
ME TO HIS MOTHER-IN-LAW, A 53 YEAR OLD
LADY TORMENTED FROM UNMOTIVATED JEALOUSY
TOWARDS HER HUSBAND WHO SHE SUSPECTED OF
HAVING AN AFFAIR WITH A YOUNGER WOMAN.

IN REALITY THE LADY'S EGO WAS SECRETLY IN LOVE WITH THE SON-IN-LAW!

BUT HER SUPER-EGO DID NOT LIKE THE IDEA VERY MUCH!

THE EGO AND SUPER-EGO
FOUND A COMPROMISE:
THE LADY COULD ALWAYS
THINK OF A SEXUAL
RELATIONSHIP...

...BETWEEN A YOUNG GUY AND AN OLD ONE
(THE OTHER WOMAN AND HER HUSBAND) A VERY EXCITING IDEA
BECAUSE IT REMINDED HER OF THE SECRET LOVE SHE HAD FOR
HER SON-IN-LAW. BUT THIS WAY SHE WAS PAYING HER PRICE
TO THE SUPER-EGO BY SUFFERING GREATLY OF JEALOUSY!
THE EGO DID NOT UNDERSTAND ANYTHING!

WHAT I DESCRIBED TO YOU WAS A SIMPLE CASE BUT ALSO THERE ARE SOME VERY COMPLICATED CASES. IN THE FAMOUS CASE OF THE MAN, WITH WOLVES THE ANALYSIS REVEALED THAT THE PATIENT, WHEN HE WAS TWO YEARS OLD, SAW HIS PARENTS WHILE THEY WERE HAVING SEX AND GOT TRAUMATIZED BY THE EXPERIENCE.

BUT HOW DO YOU DISCOVER ALL OF THESE THINGS?

THE UNCONSCIOUS PSYCHIC ACTIVITIES ALWAYS LEAVE TRACKS AND CLUES: FOR EXAMPLE THE **LAPSUS**!

LAPSUS ?

YES DOCTOR. I GIVE YOU AN EXAMPLE: A PROFESSOR HAS TO ONCE AGAIN INTRODUCE ONE OF HIS COLLEAGUE'S LAST BOOK...

WHAT A BORE! NOT AGAIN THAT OLD FART BULLSHIT!

THE ACADEMIC SOLIDARITY IS SACRED!

IT IS NOT CONVENIENT TO REFUSE : HE COULD GET OFFENDED!

THE ID TOOK CONTROL OF THE SPEECH REVEALING THE PROFESSOR'S TRUE FEELING!

A GROOM THAT FORGETS TO GO TO HIS OWN MARRIAGE HAS NO EXCUSES: THE ACT REVEALS HIS TRUE INTENTIONS! IT WILL BE VERY DIFFICULT GETTING OUT THIS TYPE OF EMBARRASSMENT.

GOODBYE!

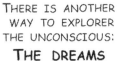

EVEN UNDER THE HARDEST TYRANNY, THERE IS ALWAYS SOMEBODY THAT COULD TELL YOU THE TRUTH: THE COURT JOKER!

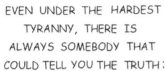

YOUR MAJESTY, YOU ARE VERY FILTHY!

THE DREAM IS THE ONE THAT CAN EXPRESS THE UNCONSCIOUS DESIRES! TO DREAM IS LIKE GOING FOR A HOLIDAY, ESCAPING FROM THE REAL WORLD, AN IRREPLACEABLE RELIEF VALVE!

BUT DREAMS ARE ILLOGICAL, WITHOUT TOP OR BOTTOM!

DOCTOR, DON'T BE SUPERFICIAL: YOU MUST MAKE A DISTINCTION BETWEEN MANIFEST CONTENT AND LATENT CONTENT OF THE DREAM!

THE MANIFEST CONTENT IS A MAN WHO DREAMS OF INFLATING HIS BIKE'S TYRE.

THE LATENT CONTENT IS HIS
MEANING: IN THIS CASE THE MAN
WISHES TO GET A WOMAN PREGNANT
TO SHOW HIS VIRILITY.
THE PUMP IS HIS PENIS!

INCREDIBLE!

OF COURSE DOCTOR: THE DREAM IS THE SATISFACTION OF AN UNCONSCIOUS DESIRE ALWAYS OF SEXUAL NATURE. ITS ILLOGIC SHAPE IS ONLY TO FOOL THE SUPER-EGO!

REGRESSION IS TO GO BACK
TO CHILDHOOD WHEN THERE ARE
DIFFICULT SITUATIONS.

THE SUBJECT GOES BACK WITH HIS MIND TO
HIS CHILDHOOD AND THE INFANTILE SEXUALITY
PHASES, WHERE HE FINDS HAPPY MEMORIES.

HE CAN'T DO ANYTHING ANYMORE.
HE WOULD LIKE OTHERS TO HELP HIM
SO HE CAN DREAM WITH HIS EYES OPEN...

BUT THE OTHERS ARE NOT WILLING!

THAT TEDDY BEAR MUST GO!

NEUROSIS IS BORN FROM THE CONTRAST BETWEEN INTERIOR LIFE AND REALITY.

THEN THE INDIVIDUAL BECOMES PREY OF ITS INTERNAL CONFLICTS!

HE CAN BECOME **DEPRESSED**

YOU ARE A PIECE OF SHIT! YOU HAVE LOST YOUR COURAGE! YOU CRY LIKE A BABY INSTEAD OF FIGHTING!

HYSTERIC

I'M THE MOST HANDSOME SOLDIER IN MY UNIT! HOLLYWOOD WOULD DEFINITELY GIVE ME THE PART OF THE INTREPID HANDSOME HERO!

IF THE ENEMIES ATTACK I'LL FAINT!

OBSESSIVE-COMPULSIVE PERSONALITY

(THE OBSESSIVE-COMPULSIVE TRIES TO
EXORCISE THE ID WITH HIS RITUALS)

AT THE POOR SOLDIER'S SOURCE OF DISFUNCTION THERE IS ALWAYS A FRUSTRATED SEXUAL DESIRE. MAYBE HE WOULD WANT TO GO HOME TO MAKE LOVE TO HIS WOMAN...

BUT IT IS A VERY DIFFICULT DESIRE TO FULFIL!

YOU DIRTY DESERTER!

BUT MR. UNCONSCIOUS, EVEN IN THE MOST FRUSTRATING SITUATIONS NOT EVERYBODY BECOMES NEUROTIC!

VERY TRUE DOCTOR! IN FACT FRUSTRATION IS ONLY THE OCCASION TO BECOME ILL! YOU TURN NEUROTIC ONLY IF YOU DON'T HAVE THE STRENGTH TO OVERCOME IT!

DO YOU SEE DOC, EVEN THE PEOPLE WE CALL NORMAL HAVE A NEUROTIC NUCLEUS, LITTLE NEUROSIS HIDDEN!

AFTER ALL THERE IS NO DIFFERENCE BETWEEN A NORMAL AND A NEUROTIC INDIVIDUAL: IT IS ONLY A QUANTITY OF MATTER!

DO YOU MEAN THAT WE ARE ALL NUTS?!

NO DOC! I MEAN THAT THE PSYCHIC CONFLICT IS NORMAL. ONLY WHEN THE CONFLICT IS TOO STRONG THAT IT LEADS TO THE SICKNESS!

BUT THINK OF WHAT I TOLD YOU AND YOU WILL HEAL YOUR PATIENTS!

NOT EVERYBODY OF COURSE! THE **PSYCHOSIS**, LIKE FOR EXAMPLE SCHIZOPHRENIA AND SOME FORMS OF DEPRESSION, ARE MENTAL SICKNESS YOU CANNOT CURE WITH THE ANALYTIC THERAPY!

WHAT'S **ANALYTIC THERAPY**?

IT IS THE METHOD YOU WILL USE TO CURE THE NEUROTICS!

Have you ever been to the dentist because your tooth aches?

Did you want to stop him while he was working on it?

...Well, yes!

THEN YOU CAN UNDERSTAND IF YOUR PATIENTS
RESIST YOU. YOU WILL BE THEIR SOUL MIRROR
BUT THEY WILL NOT WANT TO LOOK...
THEY WILL DO EVERYTHING TO OPPOSE YOUR ANALYSIS...

THEY WILL TRANSFER TO YOU THEIR UNRESOLVED
INFANTILE PSYCHIC CONFLICTS.

THE RELATIONSHIP BETWEEN A PATIENT AND ANALYST IS VERY COMPLEX: TRANSFERENCE IS AN EXAMPLE.

WHAT IS **TRANSFERENCE?**

IT IS THE PROCESS WHERE THE PATIENT "SEES" THE ANALYST AS AN IMPORTANT CHARACTER FROM HIS CHILDHOOD... IN A FEW WORDS HE THINKS HE IS HIS MOTHER OR HIS FATHER...

...THEN HE ACTS LIKE A CHILD GIVING
THE ANALYST THOUGHTS AND INTENTIONS
THAT DON'T BELONG TO HIM.

However the neurotic always will know that in reality you are not his father. Instead the psychotic, a schizophrenic for example, could lose the distinction between analysis and reality!

For this reason it is very difficult to use analytic therapy with the psychotic!

HOWEVER TRANSFERENCE IS VERY USEFUL BECAUSE IT REVEALS THE PATIENT'S INFANTILE CONFLICTS AND ALLOWS THE ANALYST TO HELP HIM RESOLVE THEM.

TRANSFERENCE ANALYSIS IS THE DECISIVE MOMENT FOR THE CURE!

BUT YOU HAVE TO BE CAREFUL AT THE **COUNTER-TRANSFERENCE**!

AND WHAT MIGHT THAT BE?

SOMETIMES IT IS THE
ANALYST THAT ACTS
LIKE A CHILD AGAINST
THE PATIENT.

BAD, BAD BOY! YOU
DON'T WANT TO
HEAL BECAUSE YOU
ARE AGAINST ME!
YOU DON'T WANT
ME TO BECOME A
GOOD, RICH AND
FAMOUS ANALYST!

THIS COULD HAPPEN IF THE ANALYST HIMSELF HAS
SOME UNRESOLVED INFANTILE CONFLICTS.
TO AVOID COUNTER-TRANSFERENCE, BEFORE HE
BECOMES AN ANALYST, IT IS NECESSARY TO UNDERGO
ANALYSIS HIMSELF FOR SEVERAL YEARS! BEFORE
YOU CAN START TO CURE OTHERS YOU NEED TO
KNOW YOURSELF!

IN FEW WORDS, MR. UNCONSCIOUS, SHOULD I ANALYZE MY PATIENTS PSYCHIC LIFE AND FIND THE TRAUMA THAT HAS MARKED THEM?

THERE IS NO TRAUMA HUNTING, DOCTOR FREUD! THE TRAUMA YOUR PATIENTS WILL TELL YOU ARE ALMOST ALWAYS INFANTILE FANTASIES!

THEY HAVE LIVED NORMAL BAD INFANTILE
EXPERIENCE AND DID NOT SUCCEED
IN DEVELOPING THEIR EGO WELL.

ANALYTIC THERAPY IS THE EGO'S GYM.

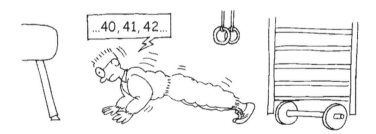

...40, 41, 42...

MANY YEARS OF ANALYTIC THERAPY PRACTICE IS
USED TO STRENGTHEN THE EGO AND PUT IT
IN CONTROL OF CONFLICTS BETWEEN THE ID
AND THE SUPER-EGO.

YOU ARE
HEALED!

I HAVE UNDERSTOOD, MR. UNCONSCIOUS:
THE ANALYST IS THE EGO'S COACH!
ITS WORK IS TO STRENGTHEN REASON
VERSUS INSTINCT!

IN SOME WAY...

IN REALITY THINGS ARE MORE COMPLICATED...
FOR EXAMPLE NOT ALL THE EGO IS CONSCIOUS...

WHAT ARE
YOU SAYING ?!

PSYCHOANALYSIS, DEAR DOC, IS A
VERY COMPLEX SCIENCE! SOME
THINGS COULD BE EXPLAINED
ONLY BY THE PSYCHOANALYSTS
UNDER FULL MOON NIGHTS!

...BUT IT
IS CRAZY!

DOC FREUD, ANALYZE YOURSELF! DO YOU BELIEVE ME NOW? ARE YOU CONVINCED?!

...YES!

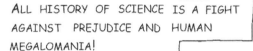

ALL HISTORY OF SCIENCE IS A FIGHT AGAINST PREJUDICE AND HUMAN MEGALOMANIA!

COPERNICUS PROVED THAT THE EARTH IS NOT THE UNIVERSE'S CENTRE BUT ONLY A TINY DOT IN SPACE!

DARWIN DEMONSTRATED THAT HUMAN KIND COMES FROM INFERIOR BIOLOGICAL FORMS AND HIS ANIMAL NATURE CAN'T BE EXCLUDED!

THEN DOC FREUD LEFT THE BASEMENT OF THE HUMAN SOUL FOR GOOD AND WENT BACK TO HIS FLAT.

IN THE NEXT YEARS HE STUDIED
HUNDREDS OF CLINICAL CASES AND
WROTE SOME BASIC TEXTS:

-THE INTERPRETATION OF DREAMS
-THE PSYCHOPATHOLOGY OF EVERYDAY LIFE
-THREE ESSAYS ON THE THEORY OF SEXUALITY
- CLINICAL STUDIES
-TOTEM AND TABOO
- THE EGO AND THE ID

SIGMUND FREUD PORTRAIT,
PSYCHOANALYSIS INVENTOR.

THAT'S ALL FOLKS!

38163717R00070

Printed in Great Britain
by Amazon